THE EGG IN THE NEST

THE TREE IN THE WOOD

Book 1

By the same editors

THE TREE IN THE WOOD
A Junior Anthology

THE EGG
IN THE NEST

Poems chosen by
RAYMOND O'MALLEY
& DENYS THOMPSON

Decorations by Julia Ball

THE TREE IN THE WOOD: BOOK 1

FRANKLIN WATTS, INC.
575 Lexington Avenue
New York, N.Y. 10022

watts
INTERNATIONAL

Copyright © Chatto and Windus Ltd 1966
Library of Congress Catalog Card Number: 68-19241

Published 1966 by
Chatto and Windus Ltd, London
First American Publication 1968
by Franklin Watts, Inc.
1 2 3 4

Printed in the U.S.A.

CONTENTS

§ 1

§ 2

§ 3

§ 4

§ 7

§ 8

The egg was in the nest,
The nest was on the twig,
The twig was on the bough,
The bough was on the tree,
The tree was in the wood;
And the green grass grew all round,
around, around,
And the green grass grew all round.

I

Solomon Grundy

Solomon Grundy,
Born on a Monday,
Christened on Tuesday,
Married on Wednesday,
Took ill on Thursday,
Worse on Friday,
Died on Saturday,
Buried on Sunday.
This is the end
Of Solomon Grundy.

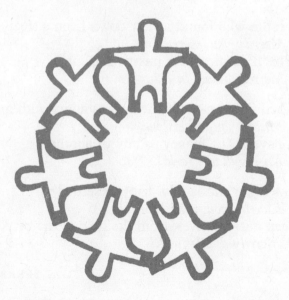

The Kettle Rhyme

'My kettle's no use any more,' mother said,
   Misery you, misery me,
And she hurled the hole-y thing over a hedge.
   Misery diddle fa-la!

A robin who found it flew down from a tree:
   Merrily you, merrily me,
'This'll do nicely for missus and me.'
   Merrily diddle fa-la!

When father came home he was angry with mother:
   Misery you, misery me,
'I haven't the money to buy us another.'
   Misery diddle fa-la!

Now robin and family, happily settled,
   Merrily you, merrily me,
Peep out—all five—from the hole in the kettle.
   Merrily diddle fa-la!

IAN SERRAILLIER

No Need

There's no need to light a night-light
On a light night like tonight,
For a night-light's a slight light
On a light night like tonight.

Cottage

When I live in a Cottage
I shall keep in my Cottage
  Two different Dogs,
  Three creamy Cows,
  Four giddy Goats,
  Five Pewter Pots
  Six silver Spoons
  Seven busy Beehives
  Eight ancient Appletrees
  Nine red Rosebushes
  Ten teeming Teapots
  Eleven chirping Chickens
  Twelve cosy Cats with their kittenish Kittens and
  One blessèd Baby in a Basket.
That's what I'll have when I live in my Cottage.

ELEANOR FARJEON

13

Dawlish Fair

Over the Hill and over the Dale,
    And over the Bourne to Dawlish,
Where ginger-bread wives have a scanty sale,
    And ginger-bread nuts are smallish.

JOHN KEATS

Tweedledum and Tweedledee

Tweedledum and Tweedledee
    Agreed to have a battle;
For Tweedledum said Tweedledee
    Had spoiled his nice new rattle.
Just then flew down a monstrous crow,
    As black as a tar-barrel;
Which frightened both the heroes so,
    They quite forgot their quarrel.

Lavender's Blue

Lavender's blue, dilly, dilly, lavender's green,
When I am king, dilly, dilly, you shall be queen;
Call up your men, dilly, dilly, set them to work,
Some to the plough, dilly, dilly, some to the cart;
Some to make hay, dilly, dilly, some to thrash corn;
Whilst you and I, dilly, dilly, keep ourselves warm.

I Saw Three Ships

I saw three ships a-sailing,
A-sailing, ay, a-sailing,
From Swansea Bay to Mandalay,
A-sailing, ay, a-sailing.
Hie away!

I saw three rogues a-riding,
A-riding, ay, a-riding,
From Bangor town to County Down,
A-riding, ay, a-riding.
Hie away!

I saw three soldiers marching,
A-marching, ay, a-marching,
From Waterloo to Timbuctoo,
A-marching, ay, a-marching.
Hie away! Hie away!

Who Has Seen the Wind?

Who has seen the wind?
  Neither I nor you:
But when the leaves hang trembling,
  The wind is passing through.

Who has seen the wind?
  Neither you nor I:
But when the trees bow down their heads
  The wind is passing by.

CHRISTINA ROSSETTI

The Jackdaw on the Steeple

There was a little jackdaw
  Lived on a vane;
He was a very black daw,
  Shiny in the rain.

There was a little church;
  It had a little steeple;
The jackdaw on his perch
  Cawed at the people.

In pops the jackdaw
  At the belfry-door;
'Caw!' says the jackdaw,
  'One peal more!'

W. B. RANDS

Who's that Bleating?

Who's that bleating
Down by the river?
Sheep are sweating,
Soon they'll shiver.
Back to farm
Without their wool,
We'll go warm,
And they'll go cool.

ELEANOR FARJEON

The City Mouse and the Garden Mouse

The city mouse lives in a house;
    The garden mouse lives in a bower,
He's friendly with the frogs and toads,
    And sees the pretty plants in flower.

The city mouse eats bread and cheese;
    The garden mouse eats what he can;
We will not grudge him seeds and stocks,
    Poor little timid furry man.

CHRISTINA ROSSETTI

17

Bed in Summer

In winter I get up at night
And dress by yellow candle-light.
In summer, quite the other way,
I have to go to bed by day.

I have to go to bed and see
The birds still hopping on the tree,
Or hear the grown-up people's feet
Still going past me in the street.

And does it not seem hard to you,
When all the sky is clear and blue,
And I should like so much to play,
To have to go to bed by day?

R. L. STEVENSON

A Song

Where the bee sucks, there suck I,
  In a cowslip's bell I lie,
There I couch when owls do cry,
On the bat's back I do fly
After summer merrily.
  Merrily, merrily, shall I live now
  Under the blossom that hangs on the bough.

WILLIAM SHAKESPEARE

The singer is a tiny fairy

I had a Little Pony

I had a little pony,
  His name was Dapple-gray,
I lent him to a lady,
  To ride a mile away;
She whipped him, she slashed him,
  She rode him through the mire;
I would not lend my pony now
  For all the lady's hire.

How many miles to Babylon?

How many miles to Babylon?
Threescore and ten.

Can I get there by candlelight?
Yes, and back again.

If your heels are nimble and light,
You may get there by candlelight.

Weather Rules

If the evening's red and the morning grey,
It is the sign of a bonnie day;
If the evening's grey and the morning's red,
The lamb and the ewe will go wet to bed.

If bees stay at home,
Rain will soon come;
If they fly away,
Fine will be the day.

A Pig Tale

Poor Jane Higgins,
  She had five piggins,
And one got drowned in the Irish Sea.
Poor Jane Higgins,
  She had four piggins,
And one flew over a sycamore tree.
Poor Jane Higgins,
  She had three piggins,
And one was taken away for pork.
Poor Jane Higgins,
  She had two piggins,
And one was sent to the Bishop of Cork.
Poor Jane Higgins,
  She had one piggin,
And that was struck by a shower of hail,
  So poor Jane Higgins,
  She had no piggins,
And that's the end of my little pig tale.

JAMES REEVES

Mice Manners

There was an Old Man of Dumbree
Who taught little Owls to drink Tea;
  For he said, 'To eat mice
  Is not proper or nice,'
That amiable man of Dumbree.

EDWARD LEAR

Three Young Rats

Three young rats with black felt hats,
Three young ducks with white straw flats,
Three young dogs with curling tails,
Three young cats with demi-veils,
Went out to walk with two young pigs
In satin vests and sorrel wigs;
But suddenly it chanced to rain,
And so they all went home again.

Fire Down Below

Fire in the galley, fire down below;
It's fetch a bucket of water, girls,
There's fire down below.

Fire, fire, fire down below,
It's fetch a bucket of water, girls,
There's fire down below.

Fire in the forepeak, fire down below;
It's fetch a bucket of water, girls,
There's fire down below.

Fire in the windlass, fire in the chain;
It's fetch a bucket of water, girls,
And put it out again.

Fire up aloft, and fire down below;
It's fetch a bucket of water, girls,
There's fire down below.

Purr

A pleasure that's
Allowed to cats
But not to citizens
Is having kittizens.

RAYMOND O'MALLEY

An Old Grace

God bless our meat,
God guide our ways,
God give us grace
Our Lord to please.
Lord, long preserve in peace and health
Our gracious Queen Elizabeth.

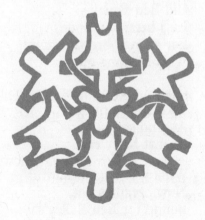

Daddy Dacon

Old Daddy Dacon
Bought a bit of bacon,
Put it on a chimney-top
For fear it would be taken.

Done For

Old Ben Bailey
He's been and done
For a small brown bunny
With his long gun.

Glazed are the eyes
That stared so clear,
And no sound stirs
In that hairy ear.

What was once beautiful
Now breathes not,
Bound for Ben Bailey's
Smoking pot.

WALTER DE LA MARE

On the Grassy Banks

On the grassy banks
Lambkins at their pranks;
Woolly sisters, woolly brothers
  Jumping off their feet
While their woolly mothers
  Watch by them and bleat.

CHRISTINA ROSSETTI

The Kangaroo

Old Jumpety-Bumpety-Hop-and-Go-One
Was lying asleep on his side in the sun.
This old Kangaroo, he was whisking the flies
(With his long glossy tail) from his ears and his eyes.
Jumpety-Bumpety-Hop-and-Go-One
Was lying asleep on his side in the sun,
Jumpety-Bumpety-Hop!

Ten Little Mice

Ten little mice sat down to spin,
Pussy passed by, and just looked in:
What are you at, my jolly ten?
We're making coats for gentlemen.
Shall I come in and cut your threads?
No, for Puss you'd bite off our heads.

My Cat

How quietly my kitty goes
Upon her softly padded toes!
The thieving mice hear not a stir
Ere they are pounced upon by her.

How neatly with her tongue so red
She licks her paw and rubs her head;
She is so cleanly and refined,
She wipes her whiskers when she's dined.

How good it is to stroke her fur,
How comforting to hear her purr.
But best of all it is when she
Steals into bed along with me.

My darling little cat I love,
All other animals above.
She shall have dainty scraps to eat
Whenever I sit down to meat.

E. L. M. KING

All Her Riches

My aunt she died a month ago,
  And left me all her riches,
A feather-bed and a wooden leg,
  And a pair of calico breeches;
A coffee-pot without a spout,
  A mug without a handle,
A baccy box without a lid,
  And half a farthing candle.

The Red Robin

Cock Robin he got a new tippet in spring,
And sat in a shed and heard other birds sing,
And he whistled a ballad as loud as he could,
And built him a nest of oak leaves by the wood. . . .

tippet, cape   JOHN CLARE

Winds for Fishing

When the wind is in the north,
Then the fishes do come forth;
When the wind is in the south,
It blows the bait in the fish's mouth;
When the wind is in the east,
Then the fishes bite the least;
When the wind is in the west,
Then the fishes bite the best.

Aiken Drum

There was a man lived in the moon,
    and his name was Aiken Drum.
And he played upon a ladle,
    and his name was Aiken Drum.

And his hat was made of good cream cheese,
    and his name was Aiken Drum.
And he played upon a ladle,
    and his name was Aiken Drum.

And his coat was made of good roast beef,
    and his name was Aiken Drum.
And he played upon a ladle,
    and his name was Aiken Drum.

And his buttons were made of penny loaves,
    and his name was Aiken Drum.
And he played upon a ladle,
    and his name was Aiken Drum.

His waistcoat was made of crust of pies,
    and his name was Aiken Drum.
And he played upon a ladle,
    and his name was Aiken Drum.

His breeches were made of haggis bags,
    anh his name was Aiken Drum.
And he played upon a ladle,
    and his name was Aiken Drum.

Rain

The rain is raining all around,
    It falls on field and tree,
It rains on the umbrellas here,
    And on the ships at sea.

R. L. STEVENSON

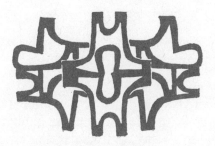

The Wind

The wind has such a rainy sound
    Moaning through the town,
The sea has such a windy sound,
    Will the ships go down?

The apples in the orchard
    Tumble from their tree.
Oh, will the ships go down, go down,
    In the windy sea?

CHRISTINA ROSSETTI

The Girl in the Lane

The girl in the lane, that couldn't speak plain,
  Cried 'Gobble, gobble, gobble';
The man on the hill, that couldn't stand still,
  Went hobble, hobble, hobble.

Monday's Child

Monday's child is fair of face,
Tuesday's child is full of grace,
Wednesday's child is full of woe,
And Thursday's child has far to go.
Friday's child is loving and giving,
And Saturday's child has to work for a living.
But the child that is born on the Sabbath day
Is bonny and lucky and wise and gay.

Three Wise Men of Gotham

Three wise men of Gotham
Went to sea in a bowl;
If the bowl had been stronger
My song would be longer.

There was a Lady

There was a lady loved a swine,
  'Honey,' quoth she,
'Pig-Hog, wilt thou be mine?'
  Hunc, quoth he.

'I'll build for thee a silver sty,
  Honey,' quoth she;
'And there in comfort thou shalt lie.'
  Hunc, quoth he.

'It shall be pinned with a silver pin,
  Honey,' quoth she,
'For latch when you go out and in.'
  Hunc, quoth he.

'Oh tell me then when we shall wed,
  Honey?' quoth she.
Hunc, hunc, HUNC, he said,
  And away went he.

Cats

Cats sleep
Anywhere,
Any table,
Any chair,
Top of piano,
Window-ledge,
In the middle,
On the edge,
Open drawer,
Empty shoe,
Anybody's
Lap will do,
Fitted in a
Cardboard box,
In the cupboard
With your frocks —
Anywhere!
They don't care!
Cats sleep
Anywhere.

ELEANOR FARJEON

Doctor Foster

Doctor Foster went to Gloster
  In a shower of rain;
He stepped in a puddle,
Right up to his middle,
  And never went there again.

St. Ives

As I was going to St. Ives,
I met a man with seven wives,
Each wife had seven sacks.
Each sack had seven cats,
Each cat had seven kits:
Kits, cats, sacks and wives,
How many were going to St. Ives?

I had a Little Nut-tree

I had a little nut-tree, nothing would it bear
But a silver nutmeg and a golden pear;
The King of Spain's daughter came to visit me,
And all for the sake of my little nut-tree.
I skipp'd over water, I danced over sea,
And all the birds in the air couldn't catch me.

Wind on the Hill

No one can tell me,
  Nobody knows,
Where the wind comes from,
  Where the wind goes.

It's flying from somewhere
  As fast as it can,
I couldn't keep up with it,
  Not if I ran.

But if I stopped holding
  The string of my kite,
It would blow with the wind
  For a day and a night.

And then when I found it,
  Wherever it blew,
I should know that the wind
  Had been going there too.

So then I could tell them
  Where the wind goes . . .
But where the wind comes from
  Nobody knows.

A. A. MILNE

Robin and Richard

Robin and Richard were two pretty men,
They lay in bed till the clock struck ten;
Then up starts Robin and looks at the sky;
'Oh, brother Richard, the sun's very high.
You go before with the bottle and bag,
And I will come after on little Jack Nag.'

The Bandog

Has anybody seen my Mopser?—
   A comely dog is he,
With hair of the colour of a Charles the Fifth,
   And teeth like ships at sea,
His tail it curls straight upwards,
   His ears stand two abreast,
And he answers to the simple name of Mopser,
   When civilly addressed.

WALTER DE LA MARE

Travelling

One leg in front of the other,
One leg in front of the other,
  As the little dog travelled
  From London to Dover.
And when he came to a stile—
Jump! he went over.

The Watch

Set a man to watch all night,
  Watch all night, watch all night,
Set a man to watch all night,
  My fair lady.

Suppose the man should fall asleep,
  Fall asleep, fall asleep,
Suppose the man should fall asleep,
  My fair lady.

Give him a pipe to smoke all night,
  Smoke all night, smoke all night,
Give him a pipe to smoke all night,
  My fair lady.

The Rain

  Rain on the green grass,
    And rain on the tree,
  And rain on the house-top,
    But not upon me!

What's Your Name?

What's your name?
  Mary Jane,
Where do you live?
  Down the lane.
What do you keep?
  A little shop.
What do you sell?
  Ginger pop.
How many bottles do you sell in a day?
Twenty-four, now go away.

The Bat

Airymouse, Airymouse, fly over my head,
And you shall have a crust of bread;
And when I brew and when I bake,
You shall have a piece of my wedding-cake.

One, Two, Buckle My Shoe

One, two,
Buckle my shoe;
Three, four,
Knock at the door;
Five, six,
Pick up sticks;
Seven, eight;
Lay them straight;
Nine, ten,
A good fat hen;
Eleven, twelve,
Dig and delve;
Thirteen, fourteen,
Maids a-courting;
Fifteen, sixteen,
Maids in the kitchen;
Seventeen, eighteen,
Maids in waiting;
Nineteen, twenty,
My plate is empty.

The Cuckoo

The cuckoo's a fine bird,
   He sings as he flies;
He brings us good tidings,
   He tells us no lies.

He sucks little birds' eggs
   To make his voice clear;
And when he sings 'Cuckoo!'
   The summer is near.

Four and Twenty Tailors

Four and twenty tailors
Went to kill a snail;
The bravest man amongst them
Durst not touch her tail;
She put out her horns
Like a little kyloe cow;
Run, tailors, run,
Or she'll kill you all e'en now!

Cock Robin

Who killed Cock Robin?
  I, said the Sparrow,
  With my bow and arrow
I killed Cock Robin.

Who saw him die?
  I, said the Fly,
  With my little eye
I saw him die.

Who caught his blood?
  I, said the Fish,
  With my little dish
I caught his blood.

Who made his shroud?
  I, said the Beetle,
  With my thread and needle
I made his shroud.

Who'll dig his grave?
  I, said the Owl,
  With my spade and trowel
I'll dig his grave.

Who'll be the parson?
  I, said the Rook,
  With my little book
I'll be the parson.

Who'll be the clerk?
  I, said the Lark,
  If not in the dark,
I'll be the clerk.

Who'll carry him to the grave?
  I, said the Kite,
  If not in the night,
I'll carry him to the grave.

Who'll carry the link?
  I, said the Linnet,
  I'll fetch it in a minute,
I'll carry the link.

link: torch

Who'll be chief mourner?
I, said the Dove,
For I mourn for my love,
I'll be chief mourner.

Who'll bear the pall?
We, said the Wren,
Both the cock and the hen,
We'll bear the pall.

Who'll sing a psalm?
I, said the Thrush,
As he sat in a bush,
I'll sing a psalm.

Who'll toll the bell?
I, said the bull,
Because I can pull,
So Cock Robin farewell.

All the birds in the air
Fell a sighing and a sobbing,
When they heard the bell toll
For poor Cock Robin.

C is for Cart

Like a blue ship the farmer's cart
Swings through the lane,
Carrying to some other part
Its load of grain,

Of logs or turnips, lambs or hay,
As case may be—
Or often on a summer day
Just you and me;

For Tom the Carter with a grin
Will always stop,
And say, 'D'ye want a lift? Hop in!'
So in we hop.

ELEANOR FARJEON

The Month of Liverpool

'Twas in the month of Liverpool
In the city of July,
The snow was raining heavily,
The streets were very dry.
The flowers were sweetly singing,
The birds were in full bloom,
As I went down the cellar
To sweep an upstairs room.

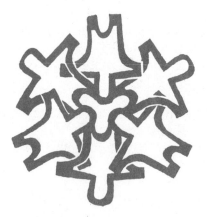

Corporal Tim

Corporal Tim
Was dressed so trim
He thought all folk afraid of him;
But sad to say,
The very first day
We had a fight,
He died of fright,
And that was the end of Corporal Tim.

The Tram

When I was younger
Than I am,
I went to Trowton
On a tram.

We made such a clanging
Banging din,
Just like a dustman
Emptying a bin.

And oh it was such a
Lovely feeling,
Sitting on top
Without a ceiling.

I wish I could sit
Up there again,
Next to the sun
And next to the rain.

But now there are no more
Trams to see. . . .
I'll tell my babies,
There used to be.

LEILA BERG

The Bells of London

Gay go up and gay go down,
To ring the bells of London town.

Halfpence and farthings,
Say the bells of St. Martin's.

Oranges and lemons,
Say the bells of St. Clement's.

Pancakes and fritters,
Say the bells of St. Peter's.

Two sticks and an apple,
Say the bells of Whitechapel.

Kettles and pans,
Say the bells of St. Ann's.

You owe me ten shillings,
Say the bells of St. Helen's.

When will you pay me?
Say the bells of Old Bailey.

When I grow rich,
Say the bells of Shoreditch.

Pray when will that be?
Say the bells of Stepney.

I am sure I don't know,
Says the great bell of Bow.

I Saw a Ship

I saw a ship a-sailing,
  A-sailing on the sea,
And oh but it was laden
  With pretty things for me.

There were comfits in the cabin,
  And sweetmeats in the hold;
The sails were made of silk,
  And the masts were made of gold.

The four-and-twenty sailors,
  That stood between the decks,
Were four-and-twenty white mice
  With chains about their necks.

The captain was a duck
  With a jacket on his back,
And when the ship began to move
  The captain said Quack! Quack!

comfits, sugar-plums

A Little Girl

When I was a little girl,
  About seven years old,
I hadn't got a petticoat,
  To keep me from the cold.

So I went into Darlington,
  That pretty little town,
And there I bought a petticoat,
  A cloak, and a gown.

I went into the woods
  And built me a kirk,
And all the birds of the air,
  They helped me to work.

The hawk, with his long claws,
  Pulled down the stone;
The dove with her rough bill,
  Brought me them home.

The parrot was the clergyman,
  The peacock was the clerk,
The bullfinch played the organ,
  And we made merry work.

A Nuisance

Last night I saw upon the stair
A little man who wasn't there;
He wasn't there again today,
Oh gee, I wish he'd go away.

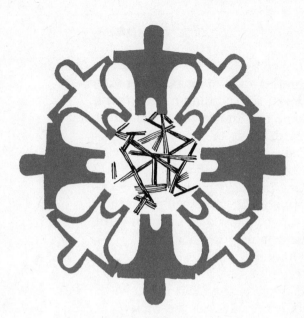

If All the Seas

If all the seas were one sea,
What a *great* sea that would be!
If all the trees were one tree,
What a *great* tree that would be!
And if all the axes were one axe,
What a *great* axe that would be!
And if all the men were one man,
What a *great* man that would be!
And if the *great* man took the *great* axe,
And cut down the *great* tree,
And let it fall into the *great* sea,
What a splish-splash that would be!

Twelve Huntsmen

Twelve huntsmen with horns and hounds,
Hunting over other men's grounds.
Eleven ships sailing o'er the main,
Some for France and some for Spain;
I wish them all safe home again.
Ten comets in the sky,
Some low and some high.
Nine peacocks in the air,
I wonder how they all come there;
I do not know and I do not care!
Eight joiners in joiner's hall
Working with the tools and all.
Seven lobsters in a dish,
As fresh as any heart could wish.
Six beetles against the wall,
Close by an old woman's apple stall.
Five puppies of our dog Ball,
Who daily for their breakfast call.
Four horses stuck in a bog;
Three monkeys tied to a clog;
Two pudding-ends would choke a dog;
With a gaping, wide-mouthed, waddling frog.

The Squirrel

Whisky, frisky,
  Hippity hop,
Up he goes
  To the tree top!

Whirly, twirly,
  Round and round,
Down he scampers
  To the ground.

Furly, curly,
  What a tail!
Tall as a feather,
  Broad as a sail!

Where's his supper?
  In the shell.
Snippity, crackity.
  Out it fell!

CHRISTINA ROSSETTI

The Old Man on the Border

There was an Old Man on the Border,
Who lived in the utmost disorder;
   He danced with the Cat,
   And made tea in his Hat,
Which vexed all the folks on the Border.

EDWARD LEAR

Early to Bed—1

Early to bed, and early to rise,
Makes a man healthy, wealthy and wise.

Early to Bed—2

Early to bed, and early to rise,
Makes a man's feet nearly double the size.

The Man of Newington

There was a man of Newington,
   And he was wondrous wise,
He jumped into a quickset hedge,
   And scratched out both his eyes:
But when he saw his eyes were out,
   With all his might and main
He jumped into another hedge,
   And scratched them in again.

Cock Robin and Jenny Wren

Little Jenny Wren
Fell sick upon a time;
Robin came to see her,
And brought her cake and wine.

'Eat well your cake, Jenny,
Drink well your wine.'
'Yes, kind Robin,
And you shall be mine.'

Jenny she got well again
And stood upon her feet,
And she told poor Robin
She loved him not a bit.

Robin he was angry
And hopped upon a twig,
Saying, 'Out upon you, fie upon you,
Bold faced jig!'

Six Old Riddles

There was a little green house—
And in the little green house
There was a little brown house,
And in the little brown house
There was a little yellow house,
And in the little yellow house
There was a little white house,
And in the little white house
There was a little heart.

A flock of white sheep
  On a red hill;
Here they go, there they go,
  Now they stand still!

As white as milk,
And not milk;
As green as grass,
And not grass;
As red as blood,
And not blood;
As black as soot,
And not soot!

I've seen you where you never were,
    And where you ne'er will be;
And yet you in that very same place
    May still be seen by me.

I had a little sister,
    They called her Pretty Peep;
She wades in the waters,
    Deep, deep, deep!
She climbs up the mountains,
    High, high, high;
My poor little sister
    She has but one eye.

Little bird of Paradise,
She works her work both neat and nice,
She pleases God, she pleases man,
She does the work that no man can.

The answers are not in the same order as the riddles: a bee, a bramble-blossom, the teeth, a star, a walnut, a face in a looking-glass.

Old Roger is Dead

Old Roger is dead and laid in his grave,
  Laid in his grave,
  Laid in his grave;
Old Roger is dead and laid in his grave,
  Hey, hi! Laid in his grave.

There grew an old apple-tree over his head,
  Over his head,
  Over his head;
There grew an old apple-tree over his head,
  Hey, hi! Over his head.

The apples grew ripe, and they all fell off,
  They all fell off,
  They all fell off;
The apples grew ripe, and they all fell off,
  Hey, hi! They all fell off.

There came an old woman a-picking them up,
  Picking them up,
  Picking them up;
There came an old woman a-picking them up,
  Hey, hi! Picking them up.

Old Roger jumps up and he gives her a knock,
  Gives her a knock,
  Gives her a knock;
Old Roger jumps up and he gives her a knock,
  Hey, hi! Gives her a knock.

He makes the old woman go hipperty hop,
  Hipperty hop,
  Hipperty hop;
He makes the old woman go hipperty hop,
  Hey, hi! Hipperty hop.

Skipping

Little Children skip,
The rope so gaily gripping,
  Tom and Harry,
  Jane and Mary,
  Kate, Diana,
  Susan, Anna,
All are fond of skipping!

The Grasshoppers all skip,
The early dew-drop sipping,
  Under, over,
  Bent and clover,
  Daisy, sorrel,
  Without quarrel,
All are fond of skipping!

The little Boats they skip,
Beside the heavy Shipping
  While the squalling
  Winds are calling,
  Falling, rising,
  Rising, falling,
All are fond of skipping!

THOMAS HOOD

Alas, Alack

Ann, Ann!
   Come! Quick as you can!
There's a fish that *talks.*
   In the frying-pan.
Out of the fat,
   As clear as glass,
He put up his mouth
   And moaned 'Alas!'
Oh, most mournful,
   'Alas, alack!'
Then turned to his sizzling,
   And sank him back.

WALTER DE LA MARE

He That Would Thrive

He that would thrive
   Must rise at five.
He that hath thriven
   May lie till eleven.

King Arthur

When King Arthur first did reign,
    He rul-èd like a king;
He bought three sacks of barley meal
    To make a plum puddiǹg.

The pudding it was made
    And duly stuffed with plums,
And lumps of suet put in it
    As big as my two thumbs.

The king and queen sat down to it
    And all the lords beside;
And what they couldn't eat that night
    The queen next morning fried.

The Fly

How large unto the tiny fly
  Must little things appear!—
A rosebud like a feather bed,
  Its prickle like a spear;

A dewdrop like a looking-glass,
  A hair like golden wire;
The smallest grain of mustard-seed
  As fierce as coals of fire;

A loaf of bread, a lofty hill;
  A wasp, a cruel leopard;
And specks of salt as bright to see
  As lambkins to a shepherd.

WALTER DE LA MARE

My Chair

As I was sitting in my chair
I knew the bottom wasn't there,
Nor legs nor back,
But I just sat,
Ignoring little things like that.

Calico Pie

Calico Pie,
  The little Birds fly
Down to the calico tree,
  Their wings were blue,
  And they sang 'Tilly-loo!'
  Till away they flew,
And they never came back to me!
  They never came back!
  They never came back!
They never came back to me!

Calico Jam,
  The little Fish swam,
Over the syllabub sea,
  He took off his hat,
To the Sole and the Sprat,
  And the Willeby-wat,
But he never came back to me!
  He never came back!
  He never came back!
He never came back to me!

Calico Ban,
The little Mice ran,
To be ready in time for tea,
Flippity Flup,
They drank it all up,
And dance in the cup,
But they never came back to me!
They never came back!
They never came back!
They never came back to me!

Calico Drum,
The Grasshoppers come,
The Butterfly, Beetle, and Bee,
Over the ground,
Around and round,
With a hop and a bound,
But they never came back!
They never came back!
They never came back!
They never came back to me!

EDWARD LEAR

The Cuckoo's Habits

In April
Come he will;
In May
He sings all day;
In June
He changes his tune;
In July
He makes ready to fly;
In August
Go he must.

Rushes in a Watery Place

Rushes in a watery place,
    And reeds in a hollow;
A soaring skylark in the sky,
    A darting swallow;
And where pale blossom used to hang
    Ripe fruit to follow.

CHRISTINA ROSSETTI

There Was a Man

There was a man, and his name was Dob,
And he had a wife, and her name was Mob,
And he had a dog, and he called it Cob,
And she had a cat, called Chitterabob.
  Cob, says Dob,
  Chitterabob, says Mob.
  Cob was Dob's dog,
  Chitterabob Mob's cat.

Pig, Cat and Puppy

Come hither, little piggy-wig,
  Come and learn your letters,
And you shall have a knife and fork
  To eat with, like your betters.

Come hither, little pussy-cat;
  If you will grammar study,
I'll give you silver clogs to wear
  Whene'er the weather's muddy.

Come hither, little puppy-dog;
  I'll give you a new collar
If you will learn to read and spell
  And be a clever scholar.

The Minnow

Of all the fishes great and small,
And all their kith and kin O,
I love the very best of all
The shining silver minnow.

Where bigger fish could never squeeze,
Or wag a tail or fin O,
He lives a gentleman at ease,
Does little Mr. Minnow.

I think that all but urchins' hearts
He could not fail to win O,
As in and out he gleams and darts,
The tireless, happy minnow.

But he has weaknesses like me,
He can't resist a tin O,
He is so anxious just to see
What there can be within O.

He comes still nearer, still more near,
Until at last he's in O;
And naughty boys, O dear, O dear,
Thus catch poor silly minnow.

E. L. M. KING

The Mischievous Raven

A farmer went trotting upon his grey mare,
  Bumpety, bumpety, bump!
With his daughter behind him so rosy and fair,
  Lumpety, lumpety, lump!

A raven cried, Croak! and they all tumbled down,
  Bumpety, bumpety, bump!
The mare broke her knees and the farmer his crown,
  Lumpety, lumpety, lump!

The mischievous raven flew laughing away,
  Bumpety, bumpety, bump!
And vowed he would serve them the same the next day,
  Lumpety, lumpety, lump!

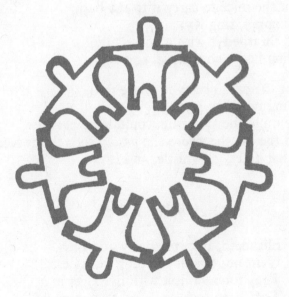

My Father Left Me Three Acres

My father left me three acres of land,
  Sing ivy, sing ivy;
My father left me three acres of land,
  Sing holly, go whistle, and ivy!

I ploughed it with a ram's horn;
  Sing ivy, sing ivy;
And sowed it all over with one peppercorn,
  Sing holly, go whistle, and ivy!

I harrowed it with a bramble bush,
  Sing ivy, sing ivy;
And reaped it with my little penknife,
  Sing holly, go whistle, and ivy!

I got the mice to carry it to the barn,
  Sing ivy, sing ivy;
And thrashed it with a goose's quill,
  Sing holly, go whistle, and ivy!

I got the cat to carry it to the mill,
  Sing ivy, sing ivy;
The miller he swore he would have her paw,
And the cat she swore she would scratch his face,
  Sing holly, go whistle, and ivy.

Another Riddle

Elizabeth, Elspeth, Betsy and Bess,
Went out one day to look for a nest;
They found a nest with five eggs in it;
They each took one, and four were left.

The Pedlar's Caravan

I wish I lived in a caravan,
With a horse to drive, like a pedlar-man.
Where he comes from nobody knows,
Or where he goes to; but on he goes.

His caravan has windows two,
And a chimney of tin, that the smoke comes through;
He has a wife, with a baby brown,
And they go riding from town to town.

Chairs to mend, and delf to sell
He clashes the basins like a bell;
Tea-trays, baskets ranged in order,
Plates, with alphabets round the border.

With the pedlar-man I should like to roam,
And write a book when I come home;
All the people would read my book,
Just like the Travels of Captain Cook.

W. B. RANDS

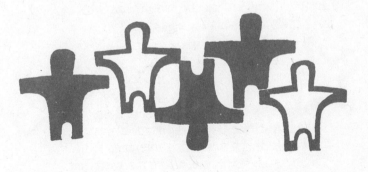

69

Blow the Wind Wester

It's up jumps the sprat, and the smallest of them all;
She jumped on the fore-deck: 'Well done, my lads all!'
So blow the wind wester, blow the wind, blow!
Our ship she's in full sail, how steady she goes.

The next came the eel with his slippery tail;
He jumped on the fore-deck and glistened the sail.

The next came the herring, the king of the sea;
He jumped on the poop: 'I'll be captain,' said he.

The next came a flat-fish; they called him the skate.
'If you be the captain, why sure, I'm the mate.'

The next came the hake, as black as a rook.
Says he: 'I'm no sailor, I'll ship as the cook.'

The next came the shark with his rolling teeth;
He said, 'Mr. Captain, shall I cook your beef?'

And then came the codfish with his chuckle-head;
He jumped in the chains, began heaving the lead.

The Difference

Big Ben strikes
Not when he likes,
   But when he is told to;
A pair of shoes
Can never choose
   Who to be sold to.

The apples inside
May never decide
   Which pie they will go in,
Nor the lilies and roses
And other posies
   Which garden to grow in.

Yet I and you
Mostly can do
   The things that we mean to,
And rely, when we say
What our needs are today,
   On having them seen to.

JOHN MASEFIELD

He! Haw! Hum!

John Cook had a little grey mare,
  He haw hum!
Her back stood up and her bones were bare.
  He haw hum.

John Cook was riding up Shuter's Bank,
  He haw hum!
And there his nag did kick and prank.
  He haw hum.

John Cook was riding up Shuter's Hill,
  He haw hum!
His mare fell down and she made her will!
  He haw hum.

The bridle and saddle were laid on the shelf.
  He haw hum.
If you want any more, you must make it yourself.
  He haw hum.

The Crooked Man

There was a crooked man was once a little lad,
He hadn't any mother and he hadn't any dad,
He hadn't any home or a family tree.
Where did he come from? Don't ask me.

This little crooked lad grew up to be a man
(One leg stopped where the other one began).
He hobbled with a stick for a whole crooked mile
And found a crooked sixpence upon a crooked stile.

He ran to a shop then — a-tinkle went the bell.
'Good morning to you missus, and what do you sell?'
'I've candy and a barrow and a black silk hat.'
'None of those, thank you, I'll buy a crooked cat.'

He bought a crooked cat and it caught a crooked mouse
Pitter-patter down the gutter of an old farm-house.
'Be friends with me, mousie, there's no harm meant,
For we're all of us crooked here but me, and I'm bent.'

They jogged along together but they couldn't keep in step.
'Right turn!' said the crooked man — they turned to the left.
But he brought them at last to a little crooked house,
And he lived there for ever with the pussy and the mouse.

There was a crooked man and he walked a crooked mile,
He found a crooked sixpence upon a crooked stile.
He bought a crooked cat and it caught a crooked mouse,
And they all lived together in a little crooked house.

IAN SERRAILLIER

A Farmyard Song

I had a cat and the cat pleased me,
I fed my cat by yonder tree;
  Cat goes fiddle-i-fee.

I had a hen and the hen pleased me,
I fed my hen by yonder tree;
  Hen goes chimmy-chuck, chimmy-chuck,
  Cat goes fiddle-i-fee.

I had a duck and the duck pleased me,
I fed my duck by yonder tree;
  Duck goes quack, quack,
  Hen goes chimmy-chuck, chimmy-chuck,
  Cat goes fiddle-i-fee.

I had a goose and the goose pleased me,
I fed my goose by yonder tree;
  Goose goes swishy, swashy,
  Duck goes quack, quack,
  Hen goes chimmy-chuck, chimmy-chuck,
  Cat goes fiddle-i-fee.

I had a sheep and the sheep pleased me,
I fed my sheep by yonder tree;
  Sheep goes baa, baa,
  Goose goes swishy, swashy,
  Duck goes quack, quack,
  Hen goes chimmy-chuck, chimmy-chuck,
  Cat goes fiddle-i-fee.

I had a pig and the pig pleased me,
I fed my pig by yonder tree;
  Pig goes griffy, gruffy,
  Sheep goes baa, baa,
  Goose goes swishy, swashy,
  Duck goes quack, quack,
  Hen goes chimmy-chuck, chimmy-chuck,
  Cat goes fiddle-i-fee.

I had a cow and the cow pleased me,
I fed my cow by yonder tree;
  Cow goes moo, moo,
  Pig goes griffy, gruffy,
  Sheep goes baa, baa,
  Goose goes swishy, swashy,
  Duck goes quack, quack,
  Hen goes chimmy-chuck, chimmy-chuck,
  Cat goes fiddle-i-fee.

I had a horse and the horse pleased me,
I fed my horse by yonder tree;
   Horse goes neigh, neigh,
   Cow goes moo, moo,
   Pig goes griffy, gruffy,
   Sheep goes baa, baa,
   Goose goes swishy, swashy,
   Duck goes quack, quack,
   Hen goes chimmy-chuck, chimmy-chuck,
   Cat goes fiddle-i-fee.

I had a dog and the dog pleased me,
I fed my dog by yonder tree;
   Dog goes bow-wow, bow-wow,
   Horse goes neigh, neigh,
   Cow goes moo, moo,
   Pig goes griffy, gruffy,
   Sheep goes baa, baa,
   Goose goes swishy, swashy,
   Duck goes quack, quack,
   Hen goes chimmy-chuck, chimmy-chuck,
   Cat goes fiddle-i-fee.

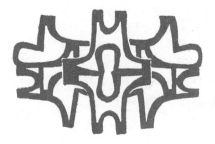

Sea-Shore

Come unto these yellow sands,
  And then take hands:
Curtsied when you have, and kissed,
  The wild waves whist,
Foot it featly here and there;
And, sweet sprites, the burden bear.
      Hark, hark!
        Bow, wow
      The watch-dogs bark,
        Bow, wow,
      Hark, hark! I hear
The strain of strutting Chanticleer
Cry, Cock-a-diddle-dow.

WILLIAM SHAKESPEARE

curtsied when you have, when you have bowed
sprites, spirits   *burden,* chorus

John and His Mare

John and his mare a journey went,
Humble, dumble, derry derry dee;
They travelled slow, by joint consent,
Tweedle, tweedle, tweedle, twinery.

They travelled near a hundred miles,
Humble, dumble, derry derry dee;
The mare jumped over all the stiles.
Tweedle, tweedle, tweedle, twinery.

It rained and blew as night came on.
Humble, dumble, derry derry dee;
Said John, 'I wish we were at home.'
Tweedle, tweedle, tweedle, twinery.

Then said the mare, 'What shall we do?'
Humble, dumble, derry derry dee;
'Good master, I have lost a shoe.'
Tweedle, tweedle, tweedle, twinery.

'Alack!' said John, 'where can we stop?'
Humble, dumble, derry derry dee;
'I do not see a blacksmith's shop.'
Tweedle, tweedle, tweedle, twinery.

At length they came to a great hall,
Humble, dumble, derry derry dee;
Where John did loudly knock and call.
Tweedle, tweedle, tweedle, twinery.

The King came out all dressed so gay,
  Humble, dumble, derry derry dee;
And begged to know what he'd to say.
  Tweedle, tweedle, tweedle, twinery.

Says John, 'I'm wet, Sir, to the skin.'
  Humble, dumble, derry derry dee;
Then said the King, 'Pray sir step in.'
  Tweedle, tweedle, tweedle, twinery.

The King brought a dry shirt for John,
  Humble, dumble, derry derry dee;
And helpèd him to put it on.
  Tweedle, tweedle, tweedle, twinery.

He introduced him to the Queen,
  Humble, dumble, derry derry dee;
As fair a dame as e'er was seen.
  Tweedle, tweedle, tweedle, twinery.

He gave him supper and a bed,
  Humble, dumble, derry derry dee;
And ordered that his horse be fed.
  Tweedle, tweedle, tweedle, twinery.

So well did John behave him there,
  Humble, dumble, derry derry dee;
The King and Queen made him Lord Mayor.
  Tweedle, tweedle, tweedle, twinery.

And now John's got a coach and four,
  Humble, dumble, derry derry dee;
I'll end my song, and sing no more.
  Tweedle, tweedle, tweedle, twinery.

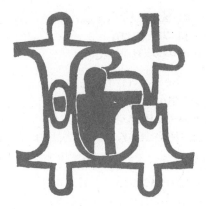

The Pets

Colm had a cat,
and a wren,
and a fly.

The cat was a pet,
and the wren
and the fly.

And it happened that the wren
ate the fly;
and it happened that the cat
ate the wren.

Then the cat died.

So Saint Colm lacked a cat,
and a wren,
and a fly.

But Saint Colm loved the cat,
and the wren,
and the fly.

So he prayed to get them back,
cat and wren;
and he prayed to get them back,
wren and fly.

And the cat became alive
and delivered up the wren;
and the wren became alive
and delivered up the fly;
and they all lived with Colm
till the day came to die.

First the cat died.
Then the wren died.
Then the fly.

ROBERT FARREN

The Twelve Oxen

I have twelve oxen that be fair and brown,
And they go a-grazing down by the town;
With hey! with how! with hoy!
Sawest not you mine oxen, you little pretty boy?

I have twelve oxen, and they be fair and white,
And they go a-grazing down by the dyke,
With hey! with how! with hoy!
Sawest not you mine oxen, you little pretty boy?

I have twelve oxen, and they be fair and black,
And they go a-grazing down by the lake,
With hey! with how! with hoy!
Sawest not you mine oxen, you little pretty boy?

I have twelve oxen, and they be fair and red,
And they go a-grazing down by the mead.
With hey! with how! with hoy!
Sawest not you mine oxen, you little pretty boy?

Index of First Lines

ACKNOWLEDGEMENTS

The editors wish to thank Geoffrey Summerfield for his suggestions. They also make grateful acknowledgment to the following for permission to reprint copyright material:

Methuen & Co Ltd for 'The Tram' from Leila Berg's *Little Pete Stories*; The Literary Trustees of Walter de la Mare and the Society of Authors as their representative for 'Done for', 'The Bandog', 'Alas, Alack' and 'The Fly'; David Higham Associates Ltd for 'Cats' and 'Who's That Bleating?' from *The Children's Bells*, 'C is for Cart' from *Country Child's Alphabet* and 'Cottage' from *Then There Were Three* by Eleanor Farjeon; Robert Farren for 'The Pets'; Methuen & Co Ltd for A. A. Milne's 'Wind on the Hill'; Basil Blackwell for 'My Cat' and 'The Minnow' by Mrs E. L. M. King; The Society of Authors and Dr John Masefield O.M. for 'The Difference'; The Clarendon Press for 'Daddy Dacon' and 'There's No Need to Light a Night Light' from *Language and Lore of Schoolchildren* by Iona and Peter Opie; James Reeves and Oxford University Press for 'A Pig Tale' from *The Blackbird in the Lilac*; Ian Serraillier and Oxford University Press for 'The Kettle Rhyme' from *The Tale of the Monster Horse* and 'The Crooked Man' from *Thomas and the Sparrow*.